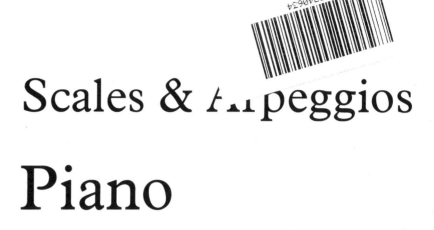

Scales & Arpeggios

Piano

Grade 6

Good legato, even fingers, firm tone and a musical curve are the essential features for playing scales and arpeggios well.

The suggested fingering shown here is not obligatory; any practical and systematic fingering which produces a good result will be accepted in the examination. Some alternative fingering is shown as follows: **4/3**. In the playing of arpeggios, the decision as to which fingering to adopt will depend on the size and shape of the player's hand. Examiners do not comment on the choice of fingering unless it interferes with an even, legato flow.

In the examination, all scales and arpeggios must be played from memory.

Metronome marks shown here indicate *minimum* recommended speeds for the examination.

Reference must always be made to the syllabus for the year in which the examination is to be taken, in case any changes have been made to the requirements.

**The Associated Board of
the Royal Schools of Music**

Major and Minor Scales (melodic *and* harmonic) in similar motion: legato
Hands separately and together an octave apart: 4 octaves: ♩ = 76

4 octaves

4 octaves

4 octaves

F# major (enharmonic G♭)

F# minor melodic

F# minor harmonic

D♭ major

C# minor melodic (enharmonic D♭)

C# minor harmonic (enharmonic D♭)

5

4 octaves

A♭ major

G♯ minor melodic (enharmonic A♭)

G♯ minor harmonic (enharmonic A♭)

E♭ major

E♭ minor melodic

E♭ minor harmonic

6

4 octaves

Major Scales (Group 1 *or* 2 at candidate's choice): staccato
Hands separately: 4 octaves: ♩ = 76

GROUP 1

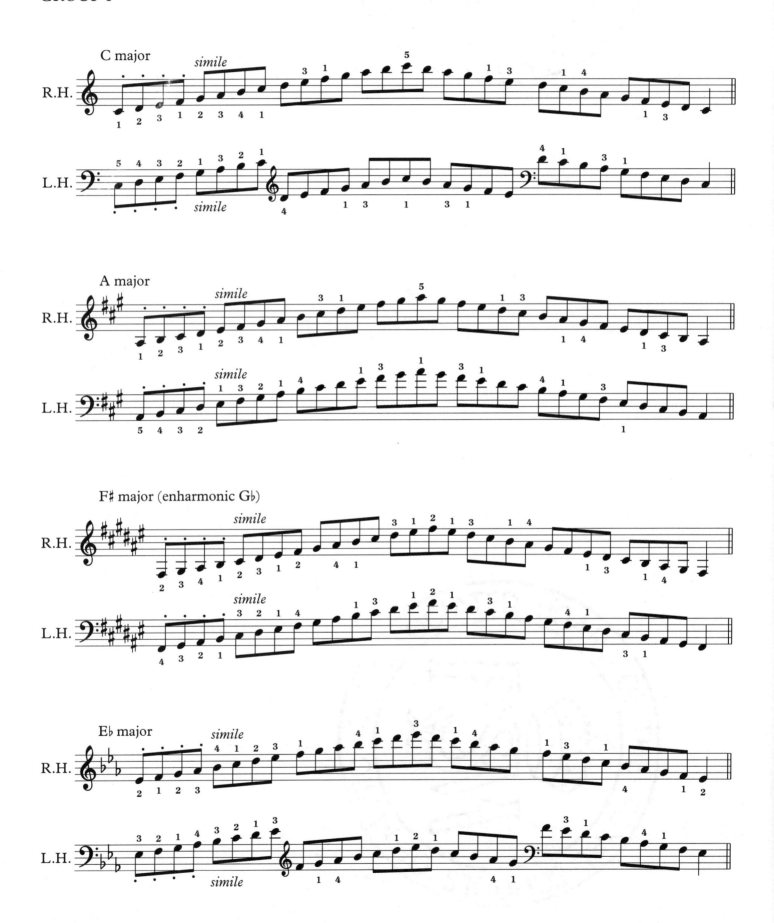

or GROUP 2

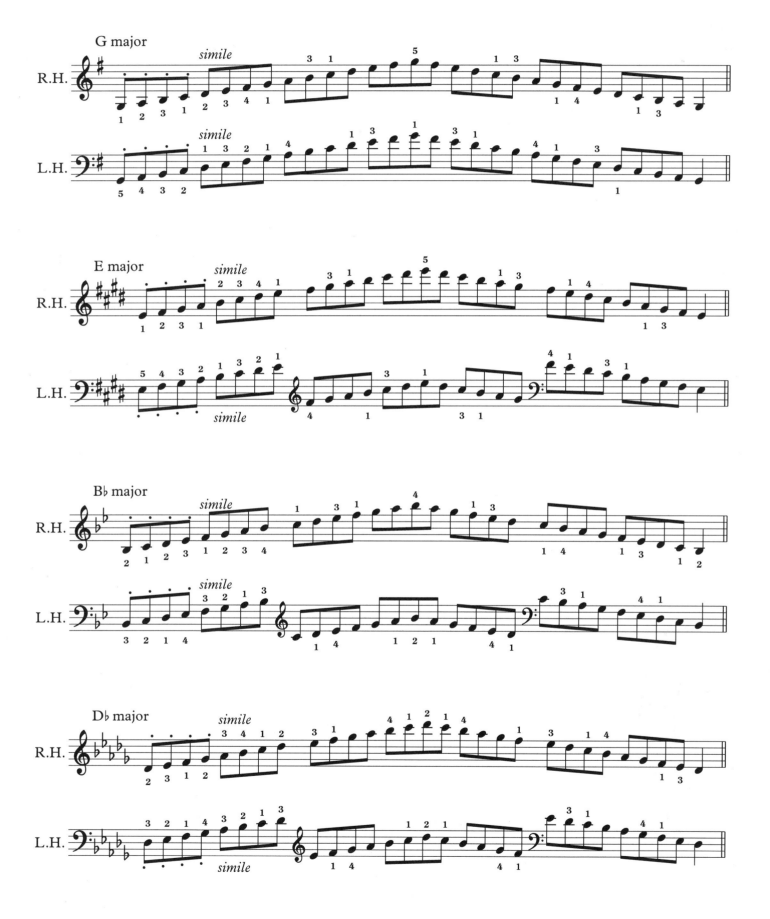

Major and Harmonic Minor Scales (same group as chosen before) in contrary motion: legato
Hands together beginning and ending on the key-note (unison): 2 octaves: ♩ = 76

GROUP 1

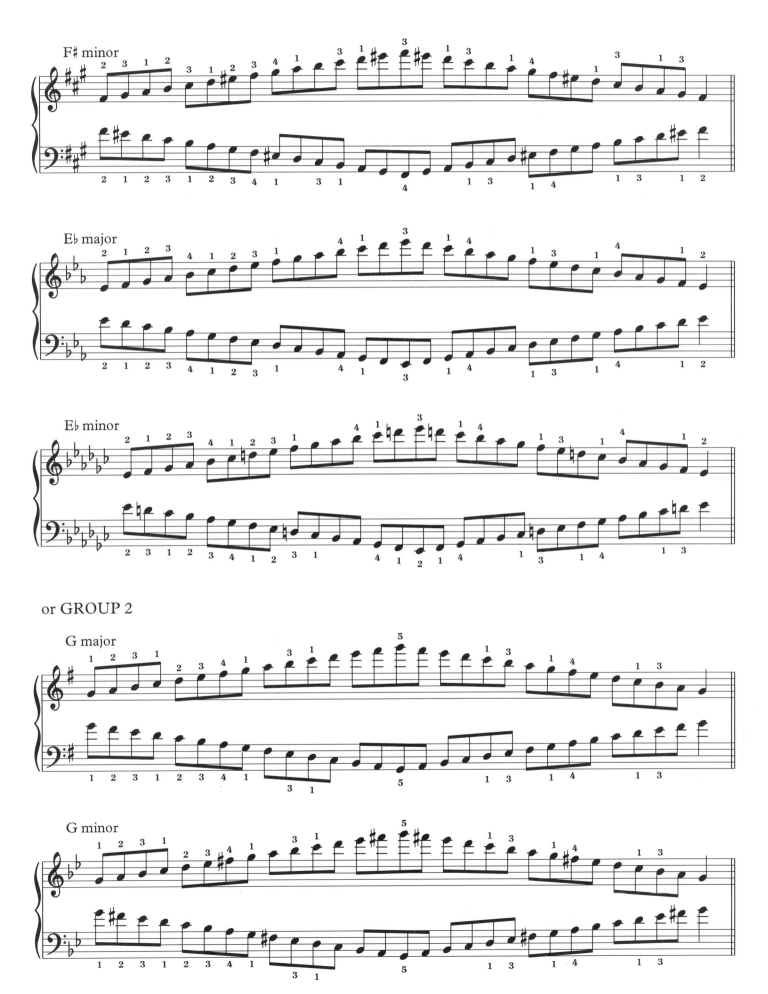

or GROUP 2

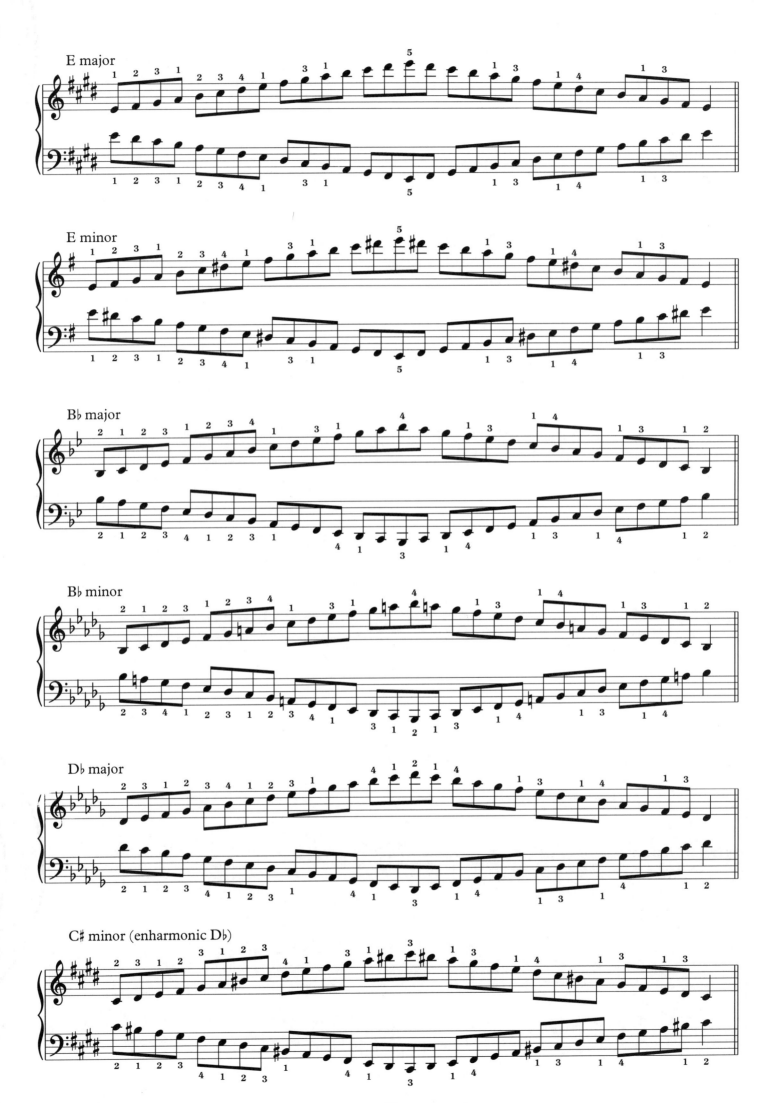

Major Scale in thirds: staccato
Hands separately: 2 octaves: ♩ = 52

Chromatic Scales in similar motion
Hands separately and together an octave apart: beginning on any note named by the examiner
4 octaves: ♩ = 76

This example is a guide

Chromatic Scale in contrary motion
Hands together: 2 octaves: ♩ = 76

Beginning on C, E

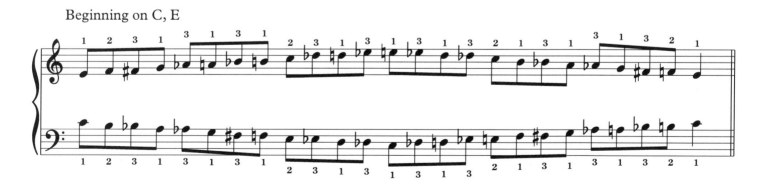

Arpeggios of major and minor common chords in root position
Hands separately and together an octave apart: 4 octaves: ♩ = 50

Arpeggios of the diminished seventh chord

Hands separately and together an octave apart: 3 octaves: ♩ = 50

Beginning on B

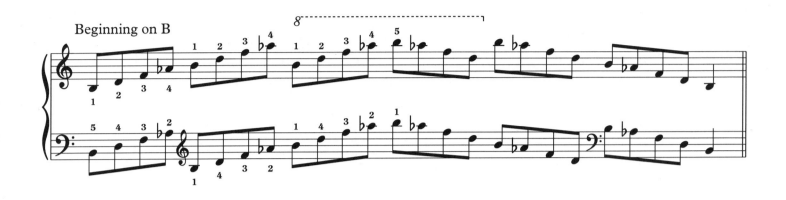

Beginning on C♯

Beginning on D♯

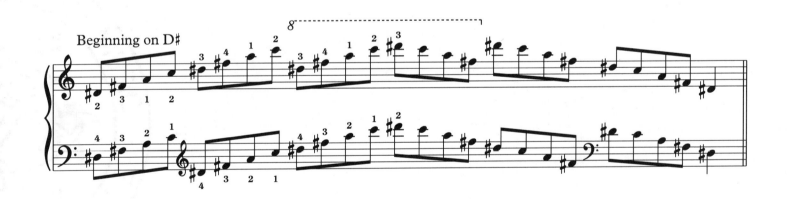

Beginning on E

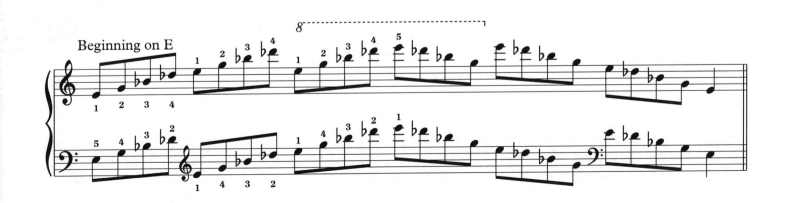

Printed in Great Britain by Headley Brothers Ltd., The Invicta Press, Ashford, Kent and London.

8/94